Magic Mates

and the
Jungle Drums

Jane West

RISING STARS

Rising Stars UK Ltd.
22 Grafton Street, London W1S 4EX
www.risingstars-uk.com

The right of Jane West to be identified as the author of this work has been
asserted by her in accordance with the Copyright, Design and Patents Act
1988.

Published 2008

Text, design and layout © Rising Stars UK Ltd.

Cover design: Button plc
Illustrator: Stik, Bill Greenhead for Illustration
Text design and typesetting: Andy Wilson
Publisher: Gill Budgell
Editor: Jane Wood

British Library Cataloguing in Publication Data.
A CIP record for this book is available from the British Library

ISBN: 982 1 84680 332 1

Printed in the UK by CPI Bookmarque, Croydon, CR0 4TD

Mixed Sources
Product group from well-managed
forests and other controlled sources
www.fsc.org Cert no. TT-COC-002227
© 1996 Forest Stewardship Council
FSC

Contents

Meet the Magic Mates

The Magic Mates are best friends –
but that doesn't mean they're all alike.

Name: *Izzie*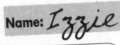

The sporty one: can climb trees, surf and take on the boys at their own game – and win.

Travels by: running!

Loves: trendy tracksuits, open skies and sandy beaches.

Hates: standing still.

Name: *Meena*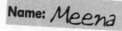

The girly one: uses her mobile for networking and planning her social life.

Travels by: Mum's car (her personal chauffeur).

Loves: pink and her Magic Mates.

Hates: breaking a nail.

Name: *Ginger*

The ginger one: you don't wanna mess with this feisty gal – the Kung Fu and quick quip queen!

Travels by: push-scooter.

Loves: Jackie Chan and her Magic Mate pals.

Hates: nail extensions.

Name: Jo

The clever one: uses her brains and quick wit to talk her way out of trouble. Sometimes she's a bit too quick.

Travels by: bicycle and is designing a pair of motorised rollerblades.

Loves: Jacqueline Wilson, Cathy Cassidy and Albert Einstein.

Hates: being called 'geek', 'nerd', 'swot' or 'boffin'.

Name: 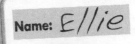 Ellie

The fashion-conscious one: can tell her Prada from her Asda and knows how to accessorise.

Travels by: limousine, of course! (But only in her dreams.)

Loves: shopping.

Hates: anything to do with getting dirty; anyone who upsets her Magic Mates.

Name: Yash

The funky punky one: the 'alternative' one of the gang who hugs trees, people and furry animals.

Travels by: skateboard.

Loves: having a good time.

Hates: bullies.

All Aboard!

The Magic Mates have won a holiday.
Lucky them! But they don't know
where they're going. It's a surprise.
Now they are sailing on a big ship
and everything is perfect. Jo thinks
it's all too good to be true …
and Jo is never wrong.

Ellie This ship is the best ever!

Meena It's got a bowling alley and a cinema!

Izzie It's got a climbing wall and a swimming pool.

Ginger It's got a gym and I can have Kung Fu lessons.

Yash   At night you can see all the stars.
It's very dark and there are
no buildings to get in the way.
It's great!

Jo   Yes, the ship is great.
But where are we going?

Ellie   It's a surprise.

Jo	I'd still like to know, so I could look it up on the Internet.
Meena	Relax and enjoy it, Jo. It's not every day we win a holiday.
Jo	OK, but I still think it's odd.

The girls enjoy their holiday on the ship.
There are so many fun things to do.

The next day, the big ship stops at
a small island. The island has a beach
of white sand and lots of palm trees.

Ellie   It's so pretty!

Meena   It's like a dream!

Izzie   I can't wait to go
and look around!

Yash   I wonder what sort of animals
this island will have?
Will there be monkeys?

Ginger   Maybe there will be lions
and tigers!

Jo   I hope not!
They might eat us!

Ellie   Whaaaaaaaat?!

Izzie   Don't worry, Ellie.
Ginger and Jo are joking.
Nothing is going to eat us.

The girls get in a motorboat and go
to the small island. When the motorboat
goes back to the ship, the girls are alone
on the island.

Ellie   Where is everyone?

Meena   Where are the shops?

Ellie	Where is the hotel?
Jo	Where are we?
Ginger	Let's have a look around.
Jo	I think we should stay here. Someone will come for us.

Rumble
in the Jungle

The girls wait. It's very sunny and they are getting hot. They are getting thirsty, too. They have only one small bottle of water to share.

Jo   This is wrong. Someone should have come by now.

Ellie   I'm so thirsty.

Jo   Can you climb that tree, Izzie?
           It has coconuts. We can drink
           coconut milk.

Izzie   That's a good idea.
           Yash, can you
           give me a hand?

Yash helps Izzie
to climb a tree.
She gets lots
of coconuts.
Now the girls
have something
to drink.

Ginger   We can't sit here all day.
I think we should go for help.

Jo   You're right. But no one
should go off alone.
Ginger and I will go this way.

Yash   Izzie and I will go that way.

Ellie   Meena and I will stay here.
If someone comes, we can
tell them where you have gone.

Izzie   Let's meet back here
in one hour.

Izzie and Yash are hot and thirsty.
As they walk across the island, there are
more and more trees. It's hard to walk
in a straight line. Soon they are lost.

Izzie   I think we're lost.

Yash   When we started walking,
the sun was on our backs.
To get back we must walk
so the sun is on our faces.

Izzie   Don't forget that the sun moves
across the sky. We could
be going the wrong way.

Yash   Oh dear. I didn't think of that.

The girls are worried and a bit scared.
Then they hear a noise in the jungle.
It is the sound of drums. There must
be people near by. Hurrah!

Yash   Can you hear that?

Izzie   Yes! Someone is playing
the drums.

Yash We just have to walk towards the noise. Then we'll be OK.

Izzie Come on, let's go!

The sound of drums gets louder.
Soon they can hear voices, too.
Some people are singing.

Izzie We're nearly there.

The drumming gets faster. Now the girls
hear a crowd all shouting together.
It sounds very fierce. It's getting louder
and louder. What is happening?
Who is chanting? They hear
someone scream.

Yash   What was that?

Izzie   I don't know, but it came
from over there.

They creep towards the sound.
They are scared now. They look
past the trees and see a terrible sight!

The girls are very scared. What can
they do? In the middle of a small village,
lots of people with fierce faces
are dancing, stamping and chanting.
Some of them are waving big sticks.
They look very scary. Suddenly,
in the middle of all the noise,
someone yells: 'CUT!'

The crowd goes even more wild. Everyone is jumping up and down and shouting.

Yash   What does he mean, 'Cut'? Cut what? What's going on?

Izzie   I don't know, but I don't like the look of it! Let's 'cut our losses' and get out of here!

Izzie   Let's go back to the others. We have to tell them.

Yash   How? We're lost!

Izzie   We have to try.

The girls turn round and go back
the way they came. When a cloud
covers the sun, they have no idea
which way to go.

Yash   Now what do we do?

Izzie   I don't know. I don't know!

They hear a noise in the jungle.
A man walks towards them. He's carrying
a big stick. He sees the girls.

Cut to the Chase

The man speaks to the girls but they
don't know what he says. He shakes
his stick at them. Then he points with it.

Yash　　I think he wants us to go that
　　　　way.

Izzie　　Shall we make a run for it?

Yash   We wouldn't get far. There are too many trees to run fast. And we're still lost.

Izzie   Let's pretend we're doing what he wants. When he's not looking, we'll run away.

Yash   That's a good idea.

The man takes them back to the village. They don't get the chance to run away.

When they get back to the village,
the crowd has stopped all the noise
and dancing. People are just standing
around chatting to each other.

Izzie   That's odd.

Yash   I don't understand.
What's going on?

They see a woman with a clipboard.
She walks towards them.

Honey   Hello, girls! My name is Honey.
Where have you been?
We were worried about you.

Yash   What's going on? We saw all
those people going wild.

Honey   Yes, they really went for it,
because it was the last scene.
It was great.

Izzie   I think I know what's going on now. You're making a film, aren't you?

Honey   Of course we are! What did you think we were doing?

Yash   I don't know, but when we heard someone shout 'Cut!' we didn't wait to see who was next for the chop!

Honey   Oh, 'cut' just means 'stop filming'. Everyone was excited because that was the end of the very last bit. Now it's time for a party.

Izzie   But it all looked so scary!

Honey   Ha, ha, ha! I'm glad you said that. It was a traditional hula dance, and it's supposed to look scary.

Izzie   I thought hula dancing was all grass skirts, flowers and smiling.

Honey   There's much more to it than that. It's very interesting.

Yash   So it seems! That man with the stick was scary, too.

Honey That's just Eddie.
He's a tour guide.

Eddie Sorry, girls! I thought you
were from my guided tour.
I show tourists around the island.
I don't want to lose anyone
in the jungle.

Yash You were really scary.

Eddie Thanks! It's really nice of you
to say that.

Yash Er … you're welcome.

Honey tells the girls that they are making
a film about something that happened
200 years ago. The star is Brad Tipp.
Keanu Rooves plays the chief
of the village.

Honey   You see, 200 years ago
the famous sailor, Captain Cook,
came to this island. The people
in the village were angry that he
had come. Captain Cook died
during a fight.

Izzie   They certainly looked angry!
I was really scared!

Honey Come and meet the stars.
We've got drinks and food.
Would you like some fresh
coconut milk?

Izzie We must get back to our friends.
We've been gone ages
and I'm worried about them.

Honey Don't worry. Your friends
are here. Ginger and Jo
found our film set an hour ago.
Then someone went to fetch
Ellie and Meena. They have
been worried about you.

Izzie and Yash follow Honey.
They are very happy that their
adventure in the jungle is over.

Yash   I'm glad our adventure is over.

Izzie   Yes, so am I.

Yash   And we've still got the rest
of our holiday to look
forward to – along with all
of our Magic Mates.

About the Author

Jane West loves bodyboarding.
She would love to go to Hawaii,
where this story is set. Then she could go
bodyboarding on the beautiful Hawaiian
beaches where surfing was first invented.

Jane West:

 lives by the beach in Cornwall

 likes taking her dog Pip paddling
in the sea

 has worked in an art gallery,
a bookshop and a school.

Now she's a writer, and has had great fun
writing about the Magic Mates. She hopes
you liked reading about them.

Hawaii

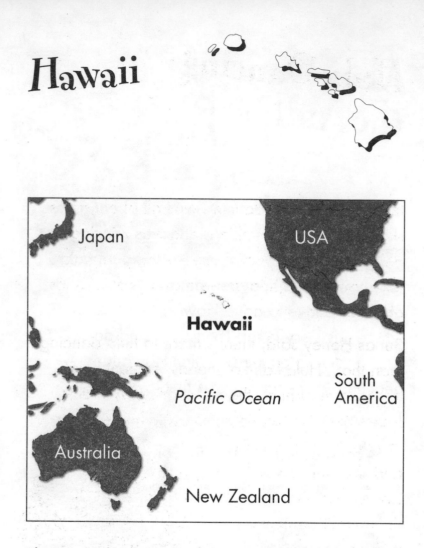

Japan

USA

Hawaii

Pacific Ocean

South
America

Australia

New Zealand

This map shows you where Hawaii is.
It's 2551 miles from America and 4687 miles
from Australia. That's a long way from anywhere!

Hula Dancing

Izzie thought hula dancing was all about grass skirts, flowers and smiling. She was thinking of 'Hula ahuana', which means 'modern hula'. This popular, joyful dance entertains thousands of tourists every year.

But as Honey said, there's more to hula dancing than that. 'Hula kahiko' means 'ancient hula'. In this form of hula, the musicians play drums, rattles and even stone castanets! The performers use dancing, chanting and drumming to tell stories from the history of Hawaii. Sometimes it looks and sounds very fierce!

Fun Facts about Hawaii

Hawaii is over 2500 miles from the USA – but it's still part of the USA.
Hawaiians have American money and American passports.

Hawaii is famous for its grass skirts, worn by men and women.

Hawaii is also famous for surfing. Surfing was invented in Hawaii over 1000 years ago.

Hawaii is more than just one island.
In fact, Hawaii is made up of eight islands.

*The last Queen of Hawaii was called
Queen Liliuokalani. She died in 1917.*

Most Hawaiian people speak English,
but some still speak the old Hawaiian
language.

*The actor Keanu Reeves is part-Hawaiian.
His first name means 'cool breeze
over the mountains' in Hawaiian.*

Captain Cook

 Captain Cook was born in 1728 in North Yorkshire and died in 1779 in Hawaii. He was a very famous and brave sailor.

 Captain Cook is famous for discovering Australia. He sailed about 12,000 miles from England to Australia in a small ship. On the way back he found the islands of Hawaii.

 Captain Cook first visited Hawaii in 1778. For the Hawaiian people, this was the season called 'Lono' which means 'peace'. At this peaceful time, the Hawaiian people were friendly towards the British sailors.

 Captain Cook returned to Hawaii several months later. The season of Lono had passed. It was now the season of 'Ku', which means 'war'. The people were angry. A fight broke out and Captain Cook was killed.

Hawaiian Lingo

aloha   hello

aloha   goodbye (Yes, it's the same as the word for 'hello'!)

mahalo please

mahalo thank you (And yes, that's the same as the word for 'please'!)

ae   yes

a'ole   no (Luckily that's not the same as the word for 'yes'! That would get really confusing!)

Quiz

1 How many islands make up Hawaii?

2 Is 'Keanu' a cool name?

3 In 1778, was it better to visit Hawaii in the season of Lono or the season of Ku?

4 Do Hawaiian people have Hawaiian passports?

5 If someone says 'Aloha' to you, are they coming or going?

Answers

1 Eight.

2 Yes, because it means 'cool breeze over the mountains'!

3 It depended whether you wanted a peaceful time, or a war! 'Lono' was the peaceful time, so that was a safer time to visit.

4 No, they have American passports because Hawaii is part of the USA.

5 Hard to say – it could mean either 'Hello' or 'Goodbye'!

Magic Mates

RISING ★ STARS

Joke Time

What do you call a hula dancer creeping through the jungle in the middle of the night?

Russell!

How did you score?

0–1 Aloha! Perhaps you should try again.

2–3 Ho'omaika'i 'ana! That means 'well done' in Hawaiian! It's a bit of a mouthful.

4–5 Hulo! That means 'hurrah!' in Hawaiian. Nice and short!